PRAISE FOR PERSONIFIED

The beauty of this mixed collection lies in its candor and earnest-ness, an artistic perspective that's intensely personal yet broadly inclusive, celebrating both humanity and the wonders of the natural world. The poems and stories in *Personified* are each a treasure hunt—gorgeous little riddles and private moments that, once revealed, inspire rereading again and again. • Lauren Mosko Bailey, former Director of Kirkus Editorial

Like Jane Hirshfield, Cherie Dawn Haas is a poet whose inspi-ration is a life thoroughly lived. With crystal clear language and warm, pastoral imagery, Haas welcomes the reader into her home with love and family, music and dance, chickens and dogs and all of the joy and heartbreak of rural life. *Personified* is a hot meal served on a cool evening, sumptuous in detail, rich in flavor, complex in its simplicity. This is a collection to cherish. • Nathan Singer, author of *The Song in the Squall and Chasing the Wolf*

Personified is a must-read poetry collection that will touch you on multiple emotional levels. Cherie Dawn Haas has a knack for peeking inside different layers of the soul and moving you to think. I highly recommend adding this book to your home library."
• Brian A. Klems, author of *Oh Boy, You're Having a Girl* (Simon & Schuster)

Personified left me breathless with awe and wonder as Cherie Dawn Haas takes you on an adventure in opening up and becoming and finding empowerment, passion, and the richness of life. She masterfully weaves poetry, stories, and prose together and takes you on a wild ride to the heart of living free and well. This book is a treasure chest of deep feelings, meaningfulness, and joy! I am changed by it—embrace her invitation and immerse yourself in the experience! • Gail McMeekin, LICSW, Creative Success LLC, author of The *12 Secrets of Highly Creative Women*, *The 12 Secrets of Highly Successful Women*, and other creativity catalyst products.

Cherie Dawn Haas's book of collected works and selected poems is an unexpected treasure. Her personal stories address universal themes that touch the heart and inspire the mind. • Jamie Markle, author and publisher

Personified by Cherie Dawn Haas is rich in an existential, sensual awareness of her relationship with and place in nature. The full spectrum of human experience and emotion is described and generously shared with her readers. Her reverence for all life is evident and honored with her words. This book will touch you in all the right places. • Sandy Prantl, author of *My Wish and Call Me Coinin*

I read the first page of *Personified* and then another and then another—and before long had swallowed the book whole. Cherie Dawn Haas' imaginative poems, stories and aphorisms drew me into a world laced with empathy, warmth and humor. Having finished the book, I closed the covers with a heart freshly opened to life's blessings and wonders. • Holly Davis, author of *Thankful Together* and Senior Editor for Golden Peak Media

PERSNIFIED

Poetry, Prose, Short Stories
& Words of Advice for Young People

CHERIE DAWN HAAS
author of the novel Girl on Fire

New Routine Press / LifeSoup.Blog

Editing by Michael Woodson

Cover art by Brianna Scharstein / briannacreative.com

For my nieces and all the young women in my life.

What do you want to do?

I believe you can.

CONTENTS

PART I

Personified

Although I've never caught one,
Today I'm going to chase birds
With the force of a Bluegrass racehorse
Like everything is relying on the outcome.

I'll also think about stealing your food
But I won't.
Instead, I'll lick your foot
Again and again until you say my name.

Surely I will nap today
Sprawled and stretched on carpet or grass
Relaxed, sometimes realizing my tongue is sticking out
I will never, never tell you, though I know you wonder,
What it is I dream about

If you slow down a minute
And stop all of your whatever-it-is-you're-doing —
Staring at things that don't move
Moving things from here to there
Disappearing for a minute behind a door
Or — the worse — for hours, off in our car
If you slow down today, I'll look in your eyes
So deeply that you'll perhaps glimpse how important
You are to me
And how critical, how life changing, I am to you.

You were there for me all through the winter
Even as early as fall
Every morning, I woke, comfortable and warm in bed
And the idea that moved my feet to the floor
Was you.
I never got sick of you. Well, the idea of you, anyway.
I took you places you weren't supposed to be—
The car, for example. I held the wheel with only one hand
Simply because I needed you in the other.
On curves, I'd even hastily put you between my knees.
The danger!
Some days, you made me shake.
But that didn't stop me from having you.
My favorite was to find you unexpectedly
At a gas station, or a mutual friend's house.
Even at night, I'd welcome your strength and warmth.
But alas!
Spring is so close that I can feel her in my hair
I'll find what I need elsewhere
And I won't need you
As much.
I'll remember you, finally, until next fall
When life fades to dormancy
And you'll be my rock again.

All my life I had feared you
So many startled awakenings when
You crept into my dreams — nightmares
Were you actually in my bed? Touching me, even?
I'll never know
Although I swear I've felt you graze my exposed thigh
In what I thought was the safest of places
My bed, my bedroom, my home
Intellectually I know that you're inherently good
And pure
So why the anxiety?
Years of anxiety.
Until I left the safety of my home
And invaded yours
Now who's afraid?
But like you, I truly mean no harm
I'm just being.
So when we meet within a breath's distance
And you can see the blue ocean of my irises
I acknowledge you and move on
And when, wearing little so I can feel the sun,
I think I feel you lightly graze my ribs
I slow down first, before reacting with violence
Is it even you there?
No, it's always just a hair.
My time in your home, and even yours in mine
Feels a little bit lighter
Now that we've come to peace
My innocent vineyard spider.

I hear you most evenings, down across the valley
As you call out to others like you
Grateful for your voice as you sing words new to me
I stop, listen, smile
I wonder if you've noticed us—this family of "other" animals
If you watched the moving truck pull into the drive
Quietly as you, we arrived
I don't hear you during mid-day, but you're there
Perhaps that's when you listen to me
Talking on the phone in a language you don't understand
But surely you don't feel threatened by my tone
Which is one of joy, usually
When our bonfire is lit, I don't hear you, so maybe
You watched me silently, recently, when I heard the words
"She died in her sleep this morning."
And I let out soft and uncontrollable cries at the
Finality, the reality, of the statement.
But, how I heard you, when I was looking for shooting stars
And your voice called so loudly that it echoed across the valley.
I was afraid for a moment...Am I dead? Is this what Heaven is?
And then I remembered things that don't happen in Heaven
But I'll take this, what has been given to me
I'll wait for your voice and withhold mine
From across the valley.

It's surprising, how many times I've seen you
Your shocking red feathers, making snow somehow seem even
　　　　more white, in contrast.
I studied you in school, the Kentucky state bird,
Winged symbol of horses and bluegrass
I think I may have ignored your voice, all these years
Because now, as I sit reading about finding—publishing—
　　　　my voice,
I feel like I've heard you for the first time.
When I finally raised my head to see who was chirping,
There you were
On a wire, crimson body making the sky somehow seem even
　　　　more blue, in contrast.
Here I am! You said
And my inked reply, in my voice, is
I am here, now.

You came unexpectedly
While I checked out at the store:
Southern States — for seeds and chicken feed.
Small town biz, we all know each other there.
Maybe I knew you were coming
Honestly, the clerk did first,
Even apologizing
As I kept walking toward the door,
Ten pounds of feed in my arms, like a baby.
We were laughing, because that's what you do
To ease or hide or ignore the pain.
Even as we joked ... the more we joked,
The more I sensed you
Knew in my heart you were close and
Overdue.
When you came, I was walking out the door,
To get safely into my car
To remember that you're okay
You make me human
You are sacred
So I let you touch my face
Then felt the memory of the path as it dried.
Felt the memory of a loved one who died
Honored her and honored you,
My unexpected tears.

You were there for me every day
Every night
Keeping me company on winding roads
On the shortest runs and the longest walks
Sometimes you would surprise me
By bringing up moments I had long forgotten
Or suppressed.
Then you'd bring me back to the present
And it always felt good.
You had so many memories to share
Mostly of love, in all of its forms
Bigger and more complex than the word itself,
Love —
Is that what I felt for you?
Now that you're gone, I wonder
Not knowing if we'll even be reunited
You were there for me every day
Every night
Until you were not.
I looked for you in all the obvious places
For days.
Then, giving up, I turned to another
Your absence beginning to muffle
As I listen to Pandora
Instead of you, my iPod Shuffle.

We've had an interesting past
Once puberty hit, you changed
I waited years for you to go back to the way you were
Unnoticed, unremarkable, I took you for granted
When you were at your most agitated
I tried to force you to be something new
No, I did force you — I can prove
I'll admit to others, when we were younger
I held a razor to you, scraping, scraping
Few would believe it
But I was such a different person then.
Eventually you seemed to forget my transgression
And I could fake-laugh at your obstinence and unpredictability
Giving in to the reality that even my body belongs to you.
After my first child, you turned against me
At a time when I was so awed by what I could do —
Carry life, bring forth life, feed life from my own breasts.
We settled the issue and things were relatively quiet, for years
You keep, I don't know how to say it,
Screwing things up.
I must find a way to forgive you
To find the former peace I felt within
First step — take you with me under the blade
To rid this cancer from my skin.

A man kicked a horse in the face.
A horse. Soft muzzle. Bony jaw.
I saw it, not in person, but does that matter?
Countless atrocities
Make me love you more.
And so I gently push my fingers
Into the fur on your body
Probing your muscles, which are miracles
Just like mine.
I give you water. Food.
Let you see my love
All the love
That the horse will never know.
I try to make up for it —
The dog fights, the ropes, chains —
With morning walks
And extra atta-boys
        Atta-girls
Into your soft ears I bury my face
Because I'm sorry for our human race.

I keep saying that I want to be you
Singing the words, looking into your brown eyes
You know how to be in the moment
And are always so happy, beyond joyful
Except when you sleep, when you dream as faithfully as you live
I especially want to be you when I see you run
And then stop to just lie in the grass.

Then, drinking my coffee before a Saturday sunrise in October,
You, sitting next to me — being so authentically yourself —
You blinked
And I blinked
You swallowed, and I swallowed
That quickly, I realized that I am you
And if that is true, then you are me

Nothing can or will stop me from running in the grass today!
Together, we will stretch our legs and blink and swallow
You'll lick your fur,
While I brush my hair
And as the moon rises,
With the same lungs we'll breathe the same air.

I never considered myself a thief
Although once, I stole a negligee
When I was 15, and I learned my lesson.
What is ownership?
If I say it belongs to me, does it?
The trees don't know the difference —
What's yours or mine or theirs.
I try to justify my daily act
By feeding you, giving you water
Shade, sun, grass, and company
How very human of me, to think you'd want or need
My company.
I talk to you, laugh, sing.
And then I steal.
All the while thanking you for your gift
Wondering how I would feel, as a mother, a feminine spirit
A feminine body.
Rage and sorrow, forever, I'm sure.
Yet I continue, telling myself that this is good.
It's better.
It's nature, and it's natural
To collect your eggs.

It was still dark
When I paused to study you for a moment
Before getting into my car and driving to the
"Office park"
To work for the day.
Sunrise had not yet broken
Just enough light, there was,
To illuminate you, so magnificent
That it was worth it to stand still and note it
Regretfully, I thought not of you all day
Although I could have. Easily.
Back home, pruning vine after vine in near silence,
I saw you again.
It must be you, I thought
But is that possible? No, maybe?
To be the same — you had to have changed.
Only the light was different —
Rays of sun from the West instead of the East
Aren't I different, myself?
Haven't I changed, moved, paused, since this morning?
A butterfly, while I was pruning vines, landed
On my bare thigh.
I raised my hand to strike out of reflex,
After countless sweat bees have landed, tickled, stung
Butterfly stayed for many minutes, and
I changed, moved, paused,
Realizing that you are not the same
Cloud.

It happened so quickly that I barely had time to flinch
There you were, in my face
I actually screamed from the immediate, real pain
The crying followed next, the little girl inside me
Showing herself
There was so much pain
That I had no shame.

I ran inside the house, gripping my forehead
Where you stung me, just under the brim of my sun hat
Sitting down, I wiped my own tears and just let them come for a
            moment as my mind raced.
Isn't this the very symbol of life?
A timely question, as shortly I'll need to shower
For a funeral.
Another quick shock to the system,
All else fades away because of the pain.

As my forehead throbbed, I tried to reassure myself
— Because no one else can really do that for you —
That the worst was over.
I should just breathe.
And then get back to work.

I worry about you

Except when I sleep — my only break.

Then, and when I walk outside at dusk

And the silver crescent of the moon slips just out of view

And I remember, what, somewhere, I know

That you really don't matter

All that much.

Despite my obsession

Letting you drive the motivation behind

So much that I do.

        I feel.

Not always a bad thing, this obsession.

After all, I can't just forget you altogether

Because then you would win.

The worry can never cease

Except for those quiet, rare moon moments

When I remember that my soul

Is more than body

        Is more than hips.

Normally calm and relaxed,

The moment you elude me

I lose all sense of peace

Anger replaces my creativity

Take a breath and start anew, I remind myself.

Alone, I can practice yoga

      Nuzzle dogs, completely unaware

      Watch the sun's elusive heat

            burn off the remaining frost,

            coating the trees like

            powdered sugar — which reminds me —

      I can bake.

The only thing to do for now

Is to ignore my craving to look for you.

Are you back? Should I call?

Always the question — why did you disappear?

Always when we're in the middle of something.

My first reaction is that you're wasting my time

Then, slowly, as I move and snuggle and watch and bake

I remember that you are giving me time

Human acts begin to dominate my mind

Before I realize it — hours pass and I almost forget

To open my laptop and check for the internet.

I watched you enter the field
Hesitating, it took you a few moments
Until you made your way into the grass
With an occasional car driving past.
You ignore each disturbance without curiosity
You don't seem to mind the telephone pole
That is the only other sign of your predator
And you don't seem to mind me.
Are you mourning the loss of your fawn?
The hay was high when the farmer mowed
Once the bales were tossed onto trucks
I watched scavengers fly to your field
They scattered after several long moments
Having completed life's cycle in this grass
Your fawn's birth and short life, all in the past
But you've come back, perhaps out of curiosity
Gathering with your herd by the telephone pole
I honor you, for you are not a predator
Unlike the drivers, unlike me
If only I could've protected your fawn
I could've walked the field before the farmer mowed
Along each yard, ahead of the trucks
There are so many dangers awaiting.

I've used you for years now

The time slipping past so slowly, and randomly

For it wasn't a daily occurrence,

Although you were always there

In the morning, and at night.

I needed you after happy times,

Also when I was at my worst sadness

And even during the mundane.

You didn't complain.

Now, when someone I love is dying

Even as the sun warms me through the cafe window

I know I'll need you soon.

I know I'll use you.

Maybe in the morning

After I stretch, remembering reality as I wake up and

Rub my eyes, feel the forgotten mascara

I'll reach for a tissue, and

I'll reach for you.

I put my hands in prayer pose
Amid the rising fog and full moon
I stood tall, outside, breathing
It probably looked like I was praying
I should have been.
That was the plan.
Instead, petty thoughts dominated
Even as the fog moved like slow waves before me
Even as the rising sun lit the moon above.
My eyes were closed but I could still see
Misunderstandings, frustrations, and the
Dominating voice of ego saying,
"But I'm the one who's right."
Echoed by the others, who say the same.
Forgive me for seeing the moon and fog,
The beauty you put everywhere before me
And ignoring it, in my shroud of self-righteousness
I see you, moon
I feel you, fog.

The way you jump up onto all fours
After a near-slumber by my feet
You were never sleeping, just waiting
For the moment when our eyes could meet.
The click-clack of me folding my glasses
As I close my laptop and put it away
These sounds you know, for them you wait
They mean I might have a moment to play.
Anticipating my next move
You study me like no other
Oh! A sign that we're going outside!
The best way to play, free-range with each other.
I approach the door as you beat me there
Your tail wagging fast, no moment to spare
I turn the knob and you're gone into the sun
Where you stop and look back, waiting for me to come.

PART II

All of Us

I've never seen so many crickets

Having gently brushed two off my body

I no longer care if they explore my bag.

We get used to things, don't we?

Tolerance increases.

Care decreases.

Thank God this is harmless.

I have no right to claim their space, anyhow

With my irrelevant human things,

That are only in the way of the crickets

Who are on what is likely a

Very important mission

To find food

Or, if they're frisky, a mate.

And so who am I

To stand in the way of their survival?

Read quickly — I must go!

They have found a way into my sleeve —

I get the hint! I will leave.

I know I'm not the only one
Nor should I be.
But it has been a long time now
And I'm afraid you're ignoring me.
Occasionally I'll get a glimpse
When I dare to look around
Should I be so bold to go to you
Or patiently wait to be found?
You said you'd be back
Now I have to doubt
As the time grows longer by the moment
And I begin to feel left out.
The coffee cup is empty
The next refill long overdue
I paid for the bottomless cup
And so I guess I'll have to get up
From this comfortable chair at Sitwell's
And see if I can find my waiter — you.

What is the meaning of life?
The question posed online
7:30 am and I thought:
I'm not going to answer that.
Then I remembered what it feels like
To dance, write poetry, or play with a dog.
I remembered that
Maybe the meaning
Is to realize there isn't one.
As I write these words
Jazz music rehearsals create a soundtrack
Of coordinated chaos —
This is the meaning of it all
Upright bass and a high-top drum to my left,
Sax warming up to my right,
And a choir of horns from down the hall.
We are all creating
We are all creators
My meaning is not your meaning
Your beauty is not mine
It all comes together in song
Meaningful, or not.

If only I could text you and see your quick reply
If only I could tag you, and see you write "hi"
No — these are not the things you'll say
When I'm eventually gone on my birthday
I think you'll miss my laugh and smile
And it takes less than a little while
To call.
Old school.
And tell me, with your voice that I would one day miss
Even if you're not here this moment to hug or kiss
That I mean more to you than a Like or emoji
That of billions of people, there's you and me
After all, it's only once a year
That we can say happy birthday, dear.

He only caught bluegill that day, well,
Plus a small catfish that jumped off the hook as he lifted it
into the boat.
We sat there for hours on that lake
Waiting.
Our arms turning red from sun
Our hands getting dirty.
Peanut butter and jelly sandwiches were on the menu
And we shared a 2-liter of Coke
And we shared a few laughs
        a lot of smiles.
When we drifted under a honeysuckle bush
at the shore, he rowed us away
because it was full of spiders.
(I hate spiders.)
He pointed out the bullfrogs and the caterpillars,
        and I saw a goldfinch in the water's
        reflection, which I pointed out to him.
        (He loves birds.)
A goose was nesting in the woods, watching us watch each other
As we rowed past, in search of THE fishing spot.
We didn't bring any fish home that day,
But oh, what we did take away.

If all we need is love, then all I need is you
Breathing into me, pumping my heart
As I lay on your side of the bed
I think of how much I adore you
Waiting patiently for you to come home
To our home that we have together
It was a major step
Soon we'll get married
Then have babies to take care of us
When we become babies in our old age
They'll laugh at us with our tattoos
Our histories of herbs
And they'll think we're cheesy when
We still give each other butterfly kisses
And Eskimo kisses
And other kisses only we know about.

Every moment of my existence
Has been leading up to you
Your brilliance, your beauty
Every moment for you
The first steps that I took on my own two feet
Were steps to your heart, to the place we would meet
The first time I opened my eyes was not the time of my birth
It was when I looked at you, and immediately knew what your
          attention was worth
All my senses were realized as we partied around a fire
"Love" is not a strong enough word to capture this desire
I knew you were the essence—the missing piece of my being
When our eyes locked, as did our hearts, and it was our life's
          beginning.

Sitting on a front porch swing
With leaves blowing at my bare feet
Playing my acoustic as the traffic goes by
With only the moon as my audience
And the stars to hear my music
I see my breath, white as I sing
My moving fingers beginning to freeze to the strings
Headlights brush my face, but I'm invisible
Tonight.

Went to work early so I wouldn't have to stay late
Knowing she was waiting for me.
It was a Tuesday afternoon on a dead-end country road
Where Delia and I felt so free.
I'll never forget how quiet she was
And I also didn't have much to say
But we couldn't stop smiling — oh how she smiled —
              as she led us on our way.
We walked along, followed a creek
The water was oh so calm that day
And when she had the chance, she took us there,
              straight to the water to play.
I watched her dip her toes
She even bent down to drink
Looked like she started to say something
But instead gazed at the minnows and left me to think.
Down at the creek with Delia
I kicked off my shoes without a care
Down at the creek with Delia
We didn't need words for this special moment to share.
Leaves falling on us
The only movement around
Delia looked up and just sat with me
Saying I love you without a sound.
Down at the creek with Delia
Where did our time ever go
Down at the creek with Delia
Don't say I love you — just let it show.

We saw a cemetery was on the land
When we walked the property that first day
"This is sacred ground," I did say
And all in all, we wanted to stay

He mowed the cemetery that became our land
Cut the weeds, the overgrowth around the graves
Illegible writing, in the maze
1700's, one did say

I often avoid the cemetery that sanctifies this land
Walking past, I look in, honor the space
Still breathing strong, I lift my face
"Thank you," I was given one more day.

It's difficult to put into words
How it feels to see you growing up
But this is how it felt
When your first girlfriend, first date
Arrived at our house for pictures
I cried a tiny bit, then got it together
Her hair twisted in braids, roses tucked in
And you, dapper in dress pants, shirt, tie
Your blue eyes nervous
Looking into my blue eyes, excited and loving
You let me teach you to dance —
One reason I know you're so in love
First loves rarely last, and I never want
Your heart to break, so we'll ignore that for now
At this moment, which is all we ever have,
I hope you're dancing together
In the meantime, I'll add to my
15 years of memories of you
The picture of you smiling as, backlit in the sun,
You slipped a pink corsage onto her wrist
In such a picture of youth and beauty and love,
I hope you'll always
Keep that moment as well.

My mother is on her deathbed, as her mother was years ago
My brothers and I hold her hands, not wanting to let go
Our father is close by, sitting in a chair
My child is nervously playing with her hair
Mother breathes softly, silence fills the space
My husband leans over, as if to kiss her face
Her eyes are open, closing only now and then
To comfort us all, she was our strength to her end
My father is praying to his God, my brothers also clasp their hands
While I only now in respect, I won't see her in hell, or in heaven
I'll see her in the mirror, also in my child
She'll watch me from the earth, always with a smile
As her mother did for her, I know she will do for me
That is to keep in touch after death, contact me in dreams
Her eyes are closing permanently, her breath is coming to a stop
I know not from watching, but from feeling my heart drop.

Grandmother, I wish you could've seen
> The moments I was on stage
>> A crowd of two-thousand
>> Dressed in their finest
>> At our own Music Hall
> Dwayne, planting sunflowers for our chickens
>> For us
>> Boosting your great-grandsons in their music
>> Loving me
> Aaron, playing trombone, cornet, baritone
>> Studying sheet music
>> Planted in front of the music stand
>> Studying performances
>> Playing video games
>> With who we think might be his first girlfriend
> Dylan, seated at the piano
>> Learning new songs
>> Mastering the emotion of the keys
>> By the soft light of a lamp
> Rusty, Hazel, Delia — you'd love them,
>> with their little paws and excitement

Last night, your daughter told me that — in just a couple of years
— it's possible that I could become a grandmother myself.
Oh, how I laughed.
But I am 43. It's certainly not unheard of.
I'll always wish you could be here to see it all.
See the extension of yourself
We laugh and cook and garden
We sit still and pay attention to nature
Make art and play music
I think, you'd be proud.

PART III

Prose Inspired by
True Stories

GOOD DOG

I open the hatchback trunk of my Subaru, where my dog is lying, her tail unthumping, unwagging. "Let's go, girl," I say to her as I gently place the collar back on her neck, coaxing her to stand so that I could put my arms under her body and lift up, then put her on the ground. She let me, then sniffs the ground for signs of other dogs that have walked the same path before.

Which one? We couldn't decide. Each dog needed a home, a forever home. Pups and mutts, and then, a ten-week-old Australian Shepherd. Gray, white, black, fluffy, and softer than soft. *I had a dog just like that when I was young*, said another potential owner as he eyed her greedily. *We'll take her*, I said.

"We'll just need you to sign in on this sheet, and then if you don't mind, go ahead and fill out these forms so we can update our records." The receptionist's words are textbook professional, but her eyes are sympathetic. She is familiar with this moment, this appointment that dog owners and cat owners and animal owners/ lovers hope they can somehow avoid.

Pixie? I love The Pixies.

No, she doesn't look like a "Pixie."
Baby?

(An unapproving look.)

It's so hard to name an animal. To come up with what we'll always call her . . . Cowgirl?

Yes, yes, that's it. She's "Cowgirl."

Haha — "Even Cowgirl Gets the Blues." Perfect.

"She's a beautiful dog. What is she?"

"Part Aussie, part Collie. She's a good girl." I tilt my head back down to the clipboard as though it were interesting.

"One of the smartest breeds I've ever known. How old is she?"

"She's twelve and a half. She's . . . not feeling well."

A respectful silence as the other pet owner nods. Despite our … situation, I return the kindness.

"Your dog's very cute. Sweet little thing."

Then I go back to the clipboard, rewriting my unchanged name, unchanged address, unchanged phone number.

Look at her trying to get up the steps!

They're too steep for her little legs. We'll have to carry her until she's a little bigger.

The vet's assistant peeks her head into the waiting room. "Cowgirl? We're ready for you." Her eyes show regret. "Ma'am, if you don't mind, it's best to pay in advance, so you don't have to fool with it afterward."

"Of course." I fumble with my purse, my wallet, my credit card, handing over the plastic with one hand, and holding her leash with the other, feeling a sickness of remorse for having to make this choice for her, for paying to have it done.

*Sit. Siii-iiiit. Sit. SIT! Good puppy! Such a good girl! You're so
smart. You're the smartest doggie in the world!*

*Now, staaay. Stay. St— Don't move. Staaay. Stay there. (pause)
Good girl! Cowgirl, you're so good!*

Speak, quiet, down, come, wait, crawl, wave, shake, turn in a
circle, say your prayers, and balance this book on your head.
We taught her every trick we heard of. She learned every one.
She performed each with an undying willingness to please, no
matter how many times we asked or told her to do something.
Blue ribbons, trophies, endless dog treats and neck scratches
for such a good dog.

She would play hard, and sleep hard, even running in her
dreams as her paws tapped into the air while her eyes fluttered
in her slumber.

"This is never easy." The vet is kind, but that's all she can be.
"There always comes a time, and we know she's suffering. I hope
you know that you're doing the right thing."

I nod my head, knowing that if I try to say anything the tears will
be let loose. Feeling that any words from my mouth, at this time,
are reserved only for saying I love you, I love you, I'm sorry, I'll
miss you, you were such a good dog.

"I'll give you a moment." And she did, leaving the examination
room, which was filled with a thick atmosphere of grief.
    I sat on the couch, lazily lying back against the seat, flipping

through TV channels, waiting for my water to break. She stood up from her nearly permanent place at the front door, where she kept us safe from intruders and squirrels, and walked over to me, laying her long nose across the swell of my belly. She looked up at me from the corner of her eyes, as if she knew that life would forever change at any moment, although neither of us were sure exactly how.

"I know you know," I say to my dog in the exam room. She looks up at me, then puts her head down, resting it just between my knees as I lean forward and bury my face in the fur of her neck.

We should have a birthday party when he turns 10 this month. I just blinked, and here he is, in the double digits.

What'll we do with Cowgirl when the kids are here? She's too grumpy these days to let her out when there's a bunch of kids running around.

Can't we put her upstairs in the bedroom?

She can't walk up the stairs anymore.

"Are you ready, Ms. Haas?"

I nod my head. Unable to speak, I put my arms around my dog and hold her steady.

The day was made of two parts: Blue sky above and green

grass below. My dog and I sat on the bottom half of the colors, watching the clouds go by. She was off leash, unattached to anything, free to go anywhere in the world. But I knew she couldn't, and wouldn't, go far. I pet her, lying down next to me, her ears perked as various sounds came and went. Birds, a distant train, then, the sound we were waiting for, the school bus, dropping off my son. She didn't stand up to greet him, didn't run down the hill, didn't bark anymore. I scratched her neck and she thumped her tail as he came to us, dropping his backpack into the grass and falling to his knees to pet her. Knowing without knowing that something was wrong.

Hey, Cowgirl.

"Let's put her on the table. Can you lift her?"

The vet goes on to explain what I can expect in the next couple of moments. A slowness of breathing, a final sigh, maybe some slight movements. I run my hands over my dog's nose, face, head, neck, her front legs, her body, back legs, her tail. Her unwagging, unthumping tail that, for more than a decade, wagged and thumped next to me.

I whisper, "Good dog."

1   Decide if you're ready for a 13-year commitment to an animal
    that will have an undying loyalty to you. Be grateful when she
    finds you.

2   Spend weeks, months, years, doing the following: taking her
    for walks, rubbing her muscles, brushing her fur, teaching her
    tricks, watching her dream in her sleep, letting her make you
    feel safe, feeding her from the table, letting her play with other
    dogs, watching her watch you watch her, letting her make
    you smile, being grateful when she wags her tail because she
    sees you, scratching her neck, and giving her what she needs
    instead of what you need. Remember: years.

3   Help her walk when she stumbles. Bring her water and food
    when she cannot walk. Give her medicine when she is sick.

4   **Note: This is the most difficult step.** Determine if you have
    to help her pass on. No one can tell you what you want or need
    to hear because there is nothing that you want or need to hear
    that's true. You may decide it's time too early. You may decide
    it's time too late. You will feel guilty either way. You must
    come to peace with what you decide when you decide it.

5   Help your dog walk to a grassy spot in the yard, where she
    loved to lie down. Let her sit and surround her with her closest
    loved ones. Pet her. Hug her. Talk to her, and say things like, "I
    love you." "You're such a good dog." "Thank you." "I'll meet
    you on the other side."

6   When she lays her head into the grass for the last time, bury
     your face in her fur. Breathe it in, cry it out. Stay there as long
     as you need to, because it's the last. In fact, stay there longer
     than you need to.

7   Find a spot of earth that is nearby, somewhere special, or
     somewhere you can visit when you like, preferably facing the
     West, so that the sunsets will give you something both breath-
     taking and symbolic to view.

8   Use a backhoe to dig the hole. Preferably ask a friend or
     neighbor, who has done the job before, and understands the
     loss. You will find comfort in this.

9   Carry her body, held by her closest loved ones, and lay her
     in the earth, covered in a blanket. Put a rawhide next to her.
     Cover her face. Let the earth take her back.

10   Stand at the mound of earth and let your mind go where it
     needs, which will be to unexpected places. Cry when you try
     to talk. Forget what she looked like wrapped in the blanket.
     Remember instead the weeks, months, years. Watch the sunset.

PART IV

Fictional
Short Stories

"I can't believe we're even arguing about this," she said, her hands deep in the hot dishwater, as she scrubbed furiously at a dinner plate that was caked in dried spaghetti sauce. "Do you even hear yourself?"

He stood up from the table and pushed the chair in, too far, so that it hit the table itself. His backpack fell off the edge and onto the linoleum with a thud, but not before pulling his glass of water over with it. Broken glass. Shallow pool of water. A couple of mounds of rounded ice cubes.

"Oh, real nice," she said, looking over her shoulder. She went back to the plate, turning her washcloth over as if that would make it do a better job.

"I hear myself just fine," he said, ignoring the mess. "You don't hear me. You don't even see me."

"I hear you just fine!" She raised her voice, mirroring the shrillness of the broken glass that still hung in the air. Another dish to replace. More money down the drain. "You need to go to your room and cool down."

"I'm not going to my damn room, mom. I'm leaving. Forget this. You don't understand."

"If you leave this house…"

Louder and with more anger than when the chair had knocked into the table, the kitchen door slammed, creating its own audible space in the room. The air from it blew the curtain back just enough for her to see him walk onto their porch with keys in hand as a family portrait—the two of them—swung in protest on the wall, knocked off center by surprise. Not unlike her.

She knew he probably wouldn't go far. He was still her baby, after all. Always would be. Toweling the soap bubbles from her red hands, she took her hair out of its loose ponytail. Full locks fell over her shoulders, and for a moment she remembered she was a woman.

She slipped on her tennis shoes and walked out the same door as her son, telling the family dog to wait inside. She wouldn't be gone long. Didn't want even the slight inconvenience of holding a leash; she just needed a breather. The day felt different to her than to her son when he made his exit. It felt the way summer should feel. Warm sun. The kind of afternoon where a peaceful walk was the cure for a mother who was cooling down after an argument with her teenager.

It would all work out. It always did.

He was a good boy. Good grades. Good friends. She knew he loved her, from his thoughtful gifts on Mother's Day, her birthday, and Christmas. He was just going through a phase. She did the same when she was a teenager (sorry, mom, she would always think when she remembered her own growing pains).

He hadn't gotten far. Didn't need to go far. Just felt like storming out the door would prove a point. Not that it meant he would get his way, but that knowledge was buried so deep that he couldn't access it at the moment. Could only drive, his music turned up, his windows down as he passed neighboring houses that became fewer and then stopped altogether at the river.

The river. His mom used to bring him here and they would picnic. Watch the barges go by. Talk about whether the river was up or if it was down. Watch the sun set the gentle waves on fire as it dipped down past the valley walls, their cue to leave before the space became the territory for a crowd that didn't care for moms and sons and families.

Watching the river calmed him. He closed his eyes, hands relaxing on the steering wheel. It was time to go back home. Maybe apologize. He would at least make an effort to not be such a punk to his own mom. She didn't deserve that, and he knew that once he walked into their warm kitchen, familiar with the smell of her cooking, he would say what he should have said instead of storming out. He was sorry. He didn't know why he was so mad. Being a teen was hard. There's no way she could understand.

Driving back, the houses came closer and closer together. The radio was still turned up, and now that he was more relaxed, he reached for the button to turn it down a notch. Almost home, anyway. His hands then turned the wheel so sharply, his body reacting quicker than his mind as he swerved to miss a cyclist that was on the road. The biker's neon spandex flashing by, then a horn from an oncoming truck, the silver grill and blue hood coming toward his car like a magnet, then tree bark somehow inches from his face, and finally his own horn, blaring in a continuous moan that faded into nothing.

There must have been physical pain when he died. He always assumed that it would hurt. His body, still warm in the driver's seat, seemed so foreign already. His heart was still in it, he knew, so he realized this must be what it's like to feel one's soul, completely. It was all true. There could be a heaven. He looked around at the remaining scene: the cyclist standing next to his bicycle as he talked excitedly into his cell phone, holding his face with the other hand ... the blue truck parked over a body ... his own car having tried to become one with the oak tree ... His vision drifted back to the body on the ground in a lingering act of human curiosity. It isn't just a body, however. It is his mother, lying on the sidewalk that is so very red. Her legs and arms at unnatural angles, her hair covering her face. Still raging with the passions to which only a teen can relate—passions which drive one to act without thinking anything through—he knew what he had to do.

As quickly as his soul could blink its translucent eyes, he went back to the river to meet his body before it was too late.

Watching the river calmed him. He closed his eyes, hands relaxing on the steering wheel. Of course it felt familiar; he had been here countless times. But this felt different. Eerie, like deja vu. Chills on his arms and legs, and a quiet inside his head whispering a crazy idea, to drive straight into the water. To keep the seatbelt on and just push the ball of his right foot into the pedal, stretching his leg straight, locking his knee and seeing how fast the car would go, what speed it would reach before hitting the first wave. But why would he do that? Because you have to, the voice said urgently.

But it was time to go back home. Apologize to his mom. No, he heard, don't do that. Do anything but that you piece of shit. Your mom deserves better and she'll be so much happier without you around ruining her life. If you love her, drive into the river. This will save her; it's the only way.

She didn't deserve to have him causing her angst, he knew. Maybe he could go home and walk into their warm kitchen, familiar with the smell of her cooking, and he could say what he should have said instead of storming out. It's not worth it, the voice said. Let's put an end to this now and everyone will be better off for it.

He was sorry and somehow he knew the voice in his head was right. He didn't want to drive into the river, but he felt it, the pushing on his right knee. He sucked in a gulp of air and grabbed his knee in resistance, putting both hands around the back of it, pulling it up and toward him, but the other-worldly pressure was great. His own voice in his head telling him, this is what has to be done, it's the only way to make things right, that he was more worthless than he could ever realize and it had to be stopped before he killed the one person who loved him, the one person he loved. For the first time, he realized that he could hear himself. He released the futile grip on his knee, feeling more at one with himself than he knew was possible.

Being a teen was hard.

I was sitting with my parents when my husband called my cell phone. I'm very close to them, mom and dad. Usually tell them everything, either future plans, current happenings — good and bad, and they even know 98% of my past transgressions. Maybe 95%.

It must have seemed odd to them when, although usually transparent, I answered the phone and then stood up from the couch, hearing my husband say, "I just completely lost my temper." I walked out of the living room, out of hearing distance from my parents, who were just asking me about my 3-year-old daughters and how they were doing with their potty training. As expensive as diapers were, I was hoping success was in the near future.

It wasn't strange that Shade would call me, except he always called when he was on his way home from work, and it was only 2:15 pm.

Our girls were ready for their snack — strawberries and then chocolate pudding. It was a great treat to them, as at home we didn't have "fancy" fruit or luxuries like this. Bananas were the cheapest, so that's what I tried to have on hand. Come summer we'd have more because that's when all the fruits went on sale.

If money seems to come up a lot, I apologize. It doesn't bring happiness, but life was certainly easier when we had more than we needed, when I was working at the library before our girls were born.

Shade is a garbage truck driver, going on seven years. Awesome benefits, really good pay. He told me once that I probably wouldn't recognize him at work. That as calm and kind as he is in our life, the worst of him came out when he was on his truck, where "jack-offs" made his job harder than it needed to be. A jack-off could be anyone who took something considered unreasonable to the curb, where Shade would have to hoist it into the truck.

Recliners. Carpet. Big-screen TVs. And then unappreciative, even rude customers that complain when he's unable to collect some oddball item they left out. Once it was a blood-stained mattress. He still remembers that address, and points it out any time we happen to drive by. The owner not only called to complain, but also gave Shade a colorful what—for at subsequent weekly pick-ups when he happened to be outside.

Years of this led to this phone call in my parent's living room. I waited until I had walked downstairs to the basement, out of earshot, to ask, "What's wrong?"

He sounded panicked. "I just finally lost it."

Calmness took over my voice. Shade and I were a perfect fit for each other, in that with athletic agility we could balance each other's emotions. Because to be honest, as a human and as a mom of two young humans, I lose my temper, occasionally, often, sometimes. Like with potty training. It almost seems as though my little girls, my sweet angels, are passive-aggressively pooping in their pants to intentionally … for what? To get my attention? To out-do her twin? Every mis-directed bowel movement costs us more money.

I could go back to work eventually, but not for a few years. Not until they start school. Daycare costs too much to make it worth it for me to go back just yet.

And so I responded to Shade with rationality pulled from a source beyond me, a source that told me to stay calm even though I was afraid to hear what he would say.

"Just tell me what happened, honey."

"I smashed the windshield of my truck."

"Did you have an accident?" I asked, not yet understanding and trying to hear in his voice if he was hurt, if a trip to the hospital was in my immediate future.

"No. I punched it. I punched the glass with my fist," he said.

"Are you on your way home?" I asked. It seemed like a stupid question, but I just wanted him to keep talking, telling me all of the details that I knew were important but that I couldn't prioritize.

"No. I told my boss. He just said, 'well, that's not good,' but that was it. I'm going to finish my route and then head back to the dump."

So he wasn't immediately fired. He wasn't hurt, and he still had his job as of this moment. It was a good time to remind myself that this moment is all we ever really have.

"I just wanted to call and say I love you," he said, and I knew that he meant that he needed forgiveness. He needed to tell me, and to hear me say it would be okay.

"I love you, too," I said in honesty, with no hidden animosity. "No matter what happens, we'll get through this." And as we hung up, I made a mental note to figure out how our little family would pay our bills, pay for the next bags of diapers, the future bunches of bananas.

"Everything okay?" Dad asked as I came back into the living room.

"I don't want to talk about it," I answered. "It will be, though."

Mom fed the girls their berries and pudding as I gathered our laundry from the dryer and began packing up the pieces of our life that scatter so quickly. A random sock, which I returned to the little bare foot. A favorite plush unicorn, back into damp little hands. Crayons into boxes, not-so-sacred scribbled paper into recycling.

Once fed and wiped down, cheeks kissed, Dad helped me load my girls and our things into the car. Car seats secured, Dad said goodbye as I got in and put on my seatbelt.

"Let us know if you need anything now," he said.

"I will, thanks," I said. He winked and tapped my door, and I winked back as I pulled out of the driveway, ready to return to the mental note I had made. Right. A plan.

So I could concentrate, I put on a children's CD and turned it up loud enough that my girls would sing along.

It worked.

Navigating the light traffic, I considered that if Shade lost his job, I could return to work. I would make half as much, I was sure, but it would be enough to pay our rent and buy groceries. And surely there were ways to save money that we hadn't thought of yet. Possibly.

Health insurance. We'd need insurance. It was something we skirted around as others paid hundreds each month. Shade's union dues covered our family so well I felt guilty, but now that could be gone. I didn't even know how to start to figure that out. I'd save that for later, because I could hear the girls' favorite song winding down and knew what was coming.

"Again, mama!"

I hit "repeat" as I slowed the car down for a red light, and picked up my phone from the console to text Shade, to ask if he heard any more from his boss. Was he fired? Put on a temporary leave of absence? And then the seed of anger that I knew better than to water — how could he do this to our family?

A flying unicorn broke my string of mental questions as the plush doll landed in the floorboard of the passenger side. If I went back to work, it would give me a daily break from our toddlers — hours of adult time. That might be nice. But then I would miss out on so many moments with them.

"Mama, again! Again!"

I pressed my foot against the gas pedal. "No babies, we're almost home now," I said as our driveway came into view. "Almost time to go inside. Almost time for naps." I would get to start talking in more complex sentences.

My phone lit up — a text from Shade. With my hands busy getting the girls out of the car, I read the message.

"Call me," the text said.

Sick to my stomach with the anti-climax, I transitioned the girls from the car to the house. I smiled at them even as my mind calculated our possible fate. I might have to start applying for jobs I didn't want, leading to bottled up resentment, leading to losing my own temper.

Before I could call him, I still had my work to do. If it was bad news, the longer I put it off, the better. I took my time getting the girls into their beds. Read them an extra long story to escort their thoughts into the unconscious realm of sleep, and tried to postpone thinking about how very different their lives might be tomorrow, or a year from now.

Shutting their door, I stopped in the bathroom and washed my face. Washed my hands, even brushed my teeth. And after I clipped my nails, cleaned my ears, and plucked my brows, I went to my phone, ready to find out the fate of our family.

"What did you find out?" I asked, now fully prepared to respond in relief or fury.

"They told me to finish my route," he said. "Said to take the day off tomorrow to cool off, and then come back. That's it."

Good. Relief.

"I'm so relieved," I said. Relieved, but slightly disappointed in not having a reason to vent my built-up frustration. I'd have to clean, furiously.

"I love you," Shade said. And I heard in his voice, "thank you."

"I love you, too," I said, and in my voice, I included a "you're welcome."

PART V

Words of Advice
for Young People

WORDS OF ADVICE FOR YOUNG PEOPLE

1 Use parchment paper when baking.

2 On the road, stop at a fast food place instead of a gas station. The bathrooms are almost always more clean and safe.

3 Scrape leftover food into the garbage first instead of using water pressure in the sink.

4 When it comes to older people and how we look/dress/act, know that it's not that we stopped caring, it's that we realize it doesn't matter.

5 Always keep at least a quarter of a tank of gas.

6 Use oven bags when cooking in your crockpot. (Get a crockpot.)

7 Don't take things so personal. It's rarely about you.

8 Think about how you often feel after you've been around someone. If you don't feel good, then avoid them.

9 Girls, use a clear base nail polish before putting on a layer of color.

10 Boys, be nice to girls.

11 Try using half of the cheese that a recipe calls for.

12 Girls, I don't think there's any advice that can make it easier for you to go through your teen years. Just know that it's temporary.

13 Remember that it's never too late to change.

14 If you're lucky enough to find something creative (or healthy or fun) that makes you lose track of time when you do it, then make it a priority in your life.

15 Study spiritual masters. Even if you don't reach enlightenment and/or inner peace, you're likely to get closer to it at least.

16 Check your posture.

17 You don't need as much toothpaste as the commercials show.

18 If you get enough sleep, everything else seems easier and better.

19 Back up your work.

20 Drink water, practice kindness, spend some time alone, and know that you can't change others.

21 Catch and release spiders. It's easier than you think, and it'll make you feel brave.

NOTE | The poem on page 73 about "my mother's deathbed" was a college writing assignment about what one's mother's death was like, or what we envisioned it would be like. This was my expectation, as my mother is still, thankfully, alive.

• C.D.H.

ACKNOWLEDGEMENTS

This book came together during the "stay at home" period of the COVID-19 pandemic. For weeks, my husband, sons, and I were morally confined to our little farm and left only to take neighborhood walks or buy necessities. Because of this, I first want to thank them — Dwayne, Dylan, and Aaron, for giving me the physical and mental space it takes to write and work on a creative project.

I also want to thank my family and friends, who have encouraged my writing endeavors throughout the years and especially recently. Asking about my current projects or sharing their own with me has helped keep the river flowing. Thank you Lauren Bailey, Laura Hughes, Andi Clemons, Jamie Markle, Gregory Morris, Laura Wright, Chuck Heffner, and Carol Rothenberger.

This book wouldn't have come together so seamlessly without the help of two specific friends I'm grateful for; we share a common thread of a passion for publishing and creativity. They are my cover designer, Brianna Scharstein and my editor, Michael Woodson. I thank them for saying "yes."

ABOUT THE AUTHOR

Cherie Dawn Haas is a writer and maker who loves all things that involve creativity. Her first novel was "Girl on Fire," which she published in 2016.

She lives with her husband and two sons in Kentucky, where they manage a small vineyard. On their homestead, they also care for their three dogs, Dangit Rusty, Hazel, and Delia, and a flock of chickens.

Find her online at:
LifeSoup.blog

Follow her on
Facebook: cheriedawnlovesfire
Instagram: @cheriedawnhaas

Made in the USA
Columbia, SC
24 December 2021

51828591R00059